FINDING OUT ABOUT

Food Hygiene

Hilary Tunnicliffe

The Institution of Environmental Hea

FRANKLIN WATTS
LONDON • NEW YORK • SYDNEY • TORONTO

Contents

This edition published 1991 by
Franklin Watts
96 Leonard Street
London EC2A 4RH

ISBN 0 7496 0720 3

All rights reserved
Printed in Belgium

Original edition published 1990 by
Hobsons Publishing plc
and sponsored by
the Institution of Environmental Health Officers
Chadwick House
Rushworth Street
London SE1 0QT

Copyright © 1990 Hobsons Publishing plc

A CIP catalogue record for this book is
available from the British Library

Acknowledgements

We would like to thank the following for supplying
photographic material:

Alfa-Laval Agri Ltd, Anglian Food Technology
Consortium, Anthony Blake Picture Library/
Timothy Ball, T Bain & D Parker/SPL, Burger King
(UK), J Burgess/SPL, CMB, Daily Telegraph,
A B Dowsett/SPL, Field Communications Ltd,
Flour Advisory Bureau Ltd, Foster Refrigeration,
The Guardian, Robert Harding Photo Library,
Dona Haycraft, Haywards, Hotpoint Ltd, Hulton
Picture Library, Institution of Environmental Health
Officers, Michael Joseph, Fiona King,
Leatherhead Food RA, Mary Evans Picture Library,
Georgia Mason, Milk Marketing Board, Mott
MacDonald Group, Mushroom Growers'
Association, National Dairy Council, National
Rivers Authority, Northern Foods plc, A D Smith/
Oxfam, Perrier, Punch, Rank Hovis McDougall
PLC, Sainsbury's, Schering Agriculture, Tesco
Creative Services, The Times, Today Newspaper,
Wilkins & Sons Limited

1 | Why is food hygiene so important?

We all need to eat to stay alive. We need a **balanced diet** so that we get all the different nutrients that our bodies need. A good supply of these nutrients promotes healthy growth and a well-functioning body which is more resistant to **disease**.

Food is taken into our bodies in many different forms: liquid, solid, hot or cold. It can be in a simple form such as a piece of fresh fruit, or as a complicated dish with many exotic ingredients which has taken a long time to prepare. Our bodies treat this food in the same way, eating and then **digesting** it into smaller, soluble substances so that it can be absorbed into the bloodstream and used for building materials or for fuel to provide us with energy.

The potential problem with eating is that the mouth and the rest of the digestive system can provide a way for harmful substances to enter the body. These substances could be poisonous chemicals, objects such as sharp pieces of metal or glass, or disease-causing **micro-organisms**. Micro-organisms such as **bacteria** are all around us. Millions live on us without causing any harmful effects. The skin is a very good barrier against these microbes. There are some bacteria which live inside our guts which help us to break down food – some even make vitamins which we then absorb into our bloodstream and use. Some foods, for example live yoghurt, contain large numbers of harmless bacteria. However, there are some bacteria which, if they enter our bodies, will cause disease.

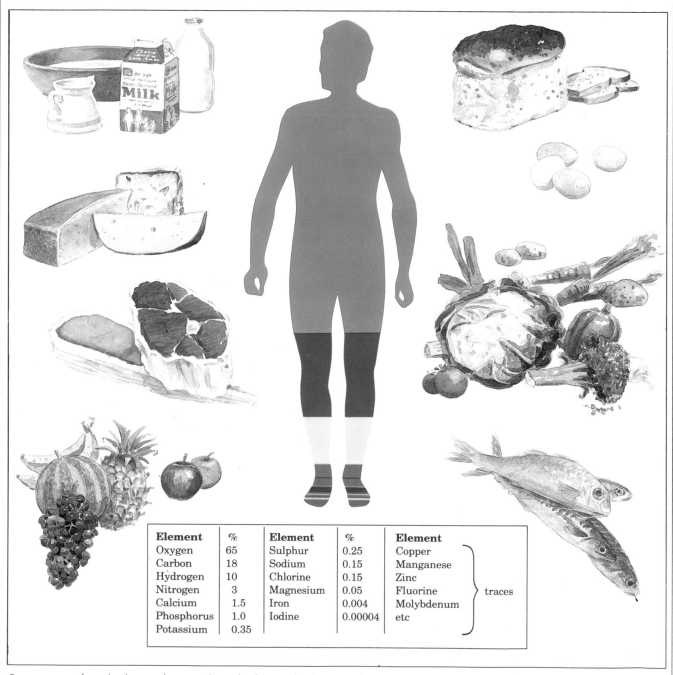

Element	%	Element	%	Element	
Oxygen	65	Sulphur	0.25	Copper	
Carbon	18	Sodium	0.15	Manganese	
Hydrogen	10	Chlorine	0.15	Zinc	
Nitrogen	3	Magnesium	0.05	Fluorine	traces
Calcium	1.5	Iron	0.004	Molybdenum	
Phosphorus	1.0	Iodine	0.00004	etc	
Potassium	0.35				

Percentage of each element by weight in the human body.

Once inside the body, these micro-organisms, poisonous substances or harmful objects are much more dangerous. Poisons can be absorbed directly into the bloodstream. Sharp objects can seriously damage the soft tissue lining the digestive system. Micro-organisms can produce substances which are poisonous to us or even start to attack the cells of our body.

The digestive system.

Mouth – saliva containing digestive enzymes is mixed with food

Oesophagus – food pipe

Liver – produces bile which is important in neutralising stomach acid and digesting fats

Gall bladder – stores bile

Pancreas – organ which produces enzymes to digest food in the small intestine

Small intestine – more enzymes are added, and digested food is absorbed through the walls and enters the bloodstream

Appendix

Anus – opening through which faeces are egested (removed from the body)

Stomach – muscular bag where food is held so that there is time to digest it. Stomach produces enzymes

Large intestine – absorbs water and some salts from the remaining unwanted food, forming faeces

Rectum – where faeces are stored before removal

Food **hygiene** is all about being careful with food. It concerns not only us, when we prepare and eat food at home, but also the people and companies involved in food production, transport and storage – in fact, every aspect of the food industry. Food hygiene is about reducing the risk of being harmed because of what we eat or drink.

Bread production.

Who makes the food safe for us to buy?

It is acknowledged that, if badly handled, treated and stored food can be a hazardous substance. However, since the early 1800s, laws have been introduced to protect the health of the public from poor quality food.

Legislation exists which controls hygiene during the slaughter of animals, and the manufacture, transportation, storage and retailing of food. Many regulations exist to control the composition and labelling of foods, the **additives** used in them and the contaminants which may affect them.

The importation of foods is also controlled and imported foods must conform to UK standards.

Environmental Health Officers

work throughout the UK at seaports and airports, and carry out inspections at slaughterhouses, food factories, hospitals, shops and restaurants to ensure that standards are met and the law is adhered to.

However, Environmental Health Officers are not as numerous as bacteria so good food hygiene practices can break down and give rise to **food poisoning**.

The avoidance of disease

'It was one of the first really good days of the summer. The family had got the barbeque out at lunchtime, and we'd raided the deep freeze. We were cooking everything – sausages, beefburgers, steaks – I even found a long-forgotten pack of chicken quarters right at the bottom of the freezer which I ate. Why does everything taste better when it's eaten outdoors?

'Twelve hours later, disaster struck! I woke up feeling really funny. I had awful tummy ache, and felt all hot and cold. I suddenly realised that I felt sick and rushed to the bathroom. For the rest of the night, I was being sick every half hour and I had chronic diarrhoea as well. No one else was ill but I kept them up all night anyway with my twice-hourly rush to the loo.

'It was about twelve hours before I could even take a little sip of water without vomiting immediately. I felt really weak for days and I still can't face the thought of chicken again...'

Food poisoning is a painful experience. **Symptoms** include abdominal pains, vomiting, diarrhoea and fever, but can be as serious as paralysis, severe **dehydration** and even death. Even mild cases of food poisoning can make healthy adults tired and generally under the weather for some considerable time. There were 54 713 cases of food poisoning reported in 1989 in England and Wales, although it is estimated that only about one case in thirty is ever reported and followed up. If we take unreported cases into consideration, a truer picture would be about 1 641 400 cases in one year alone.

4 THE DAILY TELEGRAPH, SATURDAY, FEBRUARY 17, 19

Food poisoning cases soar to a record 1,600

By David Fletcher, Health Services Correspondent

FOOD POISONING cases last month were the worst on record and urgent action is needed if an epidemic of food poisoning is to be avoided this summer, the Institution of Environmental Health Officers said yesterday. The Communicable Diseases Surveillance Centre says salmonella cases exceeded 1,600 in January

igher cent Insti- ness ntrol seri- and ches ated gave lmi- poi- the fig- tly ore . ta- ow- ce ng ve e. d ur h d y d n

SCHOOL MEAT WAS INFESTED BY MAGGOTS

MEAT destined for schools and hospitals turned out to be riddled with maggots.

The Sheffield butchers responsible for the rotting beef were fined £8,000 each yesterday. But as Norman Brammall and his son Michael left the courthouse, they began attacking waiting newsmen.

Eyewitness Alain Lockyer said: "As a TV crew followed Michael he turned and tried to karate kick and chop them.

"He grabbed hold of a sound recordist and threw him several times against a concrete pillar. Norman was screaming incoherently at the top of his voice. He tried to cover his face with a book.

"When that failed he used it as a weapon and started flailing out. They behaved like animals. Fortunately no one was badly hurt."

A meatpacking firm in Taunton, Somerset, called in health inspectors after receiving the two lorryloads of carcasses.

Barry Berlin, prosecuting, told the court: "There was a smell of decomposing meat. A bluebottle fly

SHAMED: Norman Brammall yesterday

by SIMON TRUMP

was found embedded in one forequarter.

"There were lumps of fat on the floor with dried blood and mould. One or two joints contained live maggots."

The meat had come from old and infected animals, yet had been stamped as fit for human consumption by inspectors in Barnsley, South Yorkshire, but not dated.

Health officials found only two out of a lorry-

load of 20 quarters of meat were fit to eat. In the second consignment, 31 out of 85 quarters were unfit.

Norman Brammall, 62, admitted consigning meat unfit for sale and Michael, 36, admitted a related charge. They were ordered to pay £1,520 costs.

Gerald Lumley, defending, said the prosecution was a "source of shame" for the Brammalls.

"They have lost a lot of business and have certainly learned a very expensive lesson," he added.

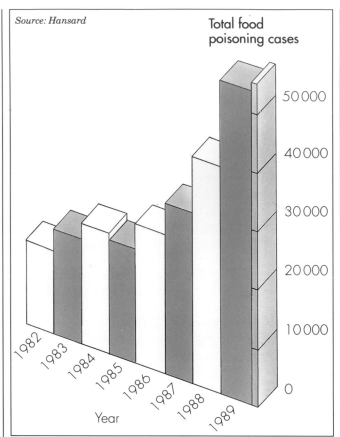

Source: Hansard

Total food poisoning cases

Cases of food poisoning in England and Wales.

WHAT YOU CAN DO

Using the graph above:

1 How many cases of food poisoning were there in 1983?

2 In which year were there the least number of cases?

It appears that the number of food poisoning incidents is still increasing, with a substantial rise being reported in each year since 1985. It has been estimated that there are about 30–40 deaths per year attributed to food poisoning.

There are several groups of people who are most likely to be seriously affected by food poisoning. These include the very young, the elderly, those who are ill already and people whose immune systems are not working properly. Some types of food poisoning are more harmful to women who are pregnant, and may affect their unborn babies.

Food poisoning is not the only illness which results from poor food hygiene. There are other diseases which are carried in food and water which can make us very ill if we take them in, for example cholera, typhoid and dysentery.

The avoidance of injury

Sometimes foreign objects are accidentally swallowed because they are present in food. This contamination can be because of poor factory maintenance, for example if a part of the machinery from a production line breaks, it may inadvertently fall into the food being produced. Objects as diverse as false teeth, diamonds from rings, even items of cutlery have been found in foods. If the foreign body is not sharp, and is small, it may go unnoticed and pass right through the digestive system. However, if the object is sharp or is made of a poisonous substance, the result can be serious – even fatal.

Recently there have been incidents of deliberate contamination of foods by certain organisations who are trying to gain publicity. Glass has been found in jars of baby food, and there have been threats that chocolate bars had been injected with a poison. Affected companies lose thousands of pounds of revenue because of incidents such as these.

PAUSE FOR THOUGHT

A manufacturer of dairy products such as yoghurts, milk puddings, milk drinks and soft cheeses received an anonymous telephone call from an animal rights organisation claiming that the company was exploiting cows. Because of this, they said they had injected some strawberry yoghurts with rat poison. An emergency board meeting was called. One director suggested that they should keep quiet but withdraw all the stocks for testing, whereas another suggested that they contact the newspapers and just ask people to look out for signs of damage or tampering. Someone suggested that they do nothing at all unless there was another 'phone call or any proof that the organisation had actually carried out their threats.

Imagine that you are one of the directors. Write out a short speech giving your reasons why you want to take the particular course of action which you have chosen.

Taking on the tin-can terrorists

The spate of food contamination cases has spawned a new crisis management industry to which companies facing at the hands vengeful for help. extortionist rompton is on a business

'A crime like this is almost impossible to detect. There are no witnesses, no fingerprints, no clues. It's down to finding somebody with a motive or information'

WHAT THE LAW SAYS
Food Safety Act, 1990

It is an offence to sell food which is unfit or not of the nature, substance or quality demanded by the purchaser.

The economic importance of food hygiene

There are many working days lost through food poisoning and illness owing to **water- or food-borne diseases**. If there has been a large-scale outbreak, this could result in the complete closure of a factory or workplace. This is costly to the employer and also to the individual, with loss of wages and overtime opportunities as factors to consider.

If a brand of food or a particular chain of stores has received bad publicity about its product, it costs thousands of pounds in lost revenue from sales. If its reputation has been damaged, it can take a long time to restore the consumer's confidence in the product. Following reports of benzene being found in bottles of Perrier water in 1989–90, the Perrier company immediately withdrew all stocks and launched a thorough investigation. Perrier sales were badly affected, and the company carried out an extensive advertising campaign to reassure its consumers that Perrier was back and safe to drink.

Elaborate advertising is used by some companies to overcome public concerns.

If an Environmental Health Officer has investigated a food outlet such as a restaurant, café or even a roadside hamburger stall, and has found it to be a health risk, he or she can take out a Prohibition Order. The officer may be visiting a premises to follow up a food poisoning outbreak, or to investigate complaints from the public, or may simply be making a routine visit. In most cases, however, the owner will be prosecuted under the Food Hygiene (General) Regulations and the owner will voluntarily close the establishment until the problems have been put right.

The act of voluntary closure obviously affects immediate trade, but some cafés or restaurants have been put out of business permanently by the adverse publicity following a successful prosecution for food hygiene offences, or by causing a major food poisoning epidemic. After all, not many people would like to go to a restaurant knowing that they could fall ill after eating their meal!

WHAT THE LAW SAYS
The Food Hygiene (General) Regulations, 1970

These regulations control the standard of hygiene within food premises. This is principally to prevent outbreaks of food poisoning. There are sections dealing with the following areas:

Premises   Washing facilities
Equipment   Services
Food handlers   Practices

Failure to maintain these standards can mean a fine of up to £2000 for each offence and in very serious cases, unlimited fines and up to two years' imprisonment.

WHAT YOU CAN DO

1 Find a map of your local area. Mark on it places that are involved in some way with food production, food storage or selling food. Colour code each type of place, eg blue for production, yellow for storage and red for retail.

2 Conduct a survey of at least fifty people of different ages. Find out:
a) how many people have suffered from food poisoning;
b) how many reported it to their doctor.

2 Food- and water-borne diseases

There are several diseases that are carried in water or food. The disease-causing microbes are taken into the body in relatively small amounts but, once inside the body in the gut, they multiply and cause serious illness by attacking the cells of the body or producing harmful **toxins** (poisons). To avoid contracting these diseases, drinking water must come from a wholesome source and fresh fruit and vegetables must be carefully washed in clean water. The microbes in dirty water may be killed by boiling. Cooking food to the correct temperature will also kill most of the microbes which cause disease.

WHAT YOU CAN DO

Look at the pictures above. Make a list of the precautions you would take if you were to eat or drink the food and water from these sources.

Food- and water-borne diseases

Typhoid

Causative organism
The bacterium responsible for typhoid is *Salmonella typhi*. It lives in the gut of **infected** people.

Symptoms
Symptoms of typhoid are varied. There may be some vomiting and diarrhoea, but not always. There is a high fever, headache, cough and a red rash on the body. The disease lasts for three to four weeks.

Method of transmission
The bacteria live in the guts of infected people and can be carried without the person feeling ill at all. They are passed on in infected faeces. In areas where there is poor sanitation, poor drainage and no water treatment, the bacteria are able to multiply in the stagnant conditions, and then infect whole communities. The bacteria can survive drying, and may be passed on through contaminated dust blowing onto other water supplies or food. Flies are vectors (carriers) of typhoid. Milk is also a common source of infection.

Brucellosis

Causative organism
Brucellosis is caused by species of the *Brucella* bacterium. There are different causative organisms depending on where you are in the world. In Britain, this is likely to be *Brucella abortus*.

Symptoms
Brucellosis causes severe sweating, fever, painful joints and headaches.

Method of transmission
Brucellosis is caught by drinking milk infected with the *Brucella* organism. It is often regarded as an occupational disease, being caught mainly by farm workers and vets. Raw milk sampling for brucellosis is carried out by Environmental Health Officers in an effort to eradicate this disease. In 1986/87 there were 3403 samples tested, and all were clear of the *Brucella* organism.

continued over

Cholera

Causative organism
Cholera is caused by a bacterium, *Vibrio cholerae*.

Symptoms
Cholera is a very serious disease which can be fatal. The symptoms of cholera are severe painless diarrhoea and vomiting, followed by very painful cramps in the arms and legs and then in the abdomen. The infected person becomes very dehydrated and weak. The second stage involves an intensification of all these symptoms, and is often fatal. Cholera is more likely to be fatal in the very young and the elderly. If patients are treated, it is likely that only 5% will die, but in an epidemic, with medical resources being stretched, the death rate can be as high as 50%.

Method of transmission
Cholera is carried in contaminated water, but can also be transmitted onto food by flies. It is usually infected human faeces which contaminate the water because of poor sanitation. Food which has been contaminated by water, flies or soiled hands can also pass on the disease. Shellfish which filter feed in infected water can also contain a high proportion of the bacteria, and so can cause cholera.

Dysentery

Causative organism
This disease is caused by species of the *Shigella* bacterium.

Symptoms
The symptoms include abdominal pain followed by diarrhoea. There may be some nausea, aching limbs and shivering. In serious cases, the intestine can be punctured, resulting in haemorrhaging.

Method of transmission
This disease is spread mainly by flies, by direct contact and by water contaminated by infected faeces. It is often contracted by eating raw vegetables or by eating food prepared by infected people.

NB: amoebic dysentery is caused by a single-celled organism (*Entamoeba histolytica*) which colonises the large intestine. It is contracted by eating contaminated food or water. Flies also pass on this form of dysentery. The symptoms are the same, but may not be obvious for a considerable time. This is a disease found in tropical and subtropical regions of the world. Most cases reported in Britain will have been contracted abroad.

Water contaminated due to poor sanitation

Contaminated water carries bacteria over long distances

Untreated water used for drinking

The cholera bacteria, *Vibrio cholerae*, are passed with the faeces from the latrine

Unprotected food may be contaminated by flies or soiled hands. Flies may enter houses through open windows or land on unprotected food left outdoors

Flies carry the *Vibrio* bacteria from faeces to food

How cholera is spread.

CASE STUDY

John Snow's study of cholera – a water-borne disease

It was noted in a report on the diseases of London, which was published in 1819, that the chief diseases were 'intermittent and remittent fevers and dysentery'. The recognised diseases were malaria, cholera and 'gaol fever' – typhus. This disease, passed on by ticks and mites, was thought to be the same disease as typhoid, a water-borne disease. It was not until 1837 that the two were distinguished, but from contemporary descriptions, both diseases thrived.

Most diseases arose from poor sanitation; sewers discharging their contents straight into the Thames, which was also used as a major source of water for washing and drinking. The Serpentine in Hyde Park was no better than an open sewer, with the waste from a large area of London draining into it. Other large towns were much the same. Manchester had many 'open cesspools, obstructed drains, ditches full of stagnant water, dunghills, pigsties, etc, from which the most abominable odours are emitted' according to a report on the sanitary conditions of the labouring population which was published in 1842. Many of the cesspools and drains overflowed frequently, making it easy to see how drinking water supplies were

contaminated. There were great cholera epidemics in Britain between 1831 and 1866 which killed thousands of people.

Doctor John Snow first put forward the theory that cholera was a water-borne disease. He collected information about outbreaks of cholera in the nineteenth century and noted that it seemed to travel from the East, and spread along the route from port to port. He worked out that the disease must increase in the infected person and must somehow be swallowed accidentally by others. He linked this to eating and drinking in unclean conditions.

Following a serious outbreak in the Broad Street region of London in 1854, Dr Snow collected information about the outbreak of cholera. He recorded the houses where people died of cholera on a map.

He traced the source of the infection to one water pump situated in Broad Street and attempted to stop further spread by removing the pump handle.

Key

A bar is placed on the house where deaths from cholera took place

Dr Snow's map, showing deaths from cholera centred around the Broad Street pump in London.

Dr Snow also noted that more than half of the deaths that occurred in another outbreak were of people who worked on the Thames and relied on the river for their drinking water. A topical cartoon in Punch described cholera, diphtheria and scrofula (a type of tuberculosis) as the three sons of the Thames.

FATHER THAMES INTRODUCING HIS OFFSPRING TO THE FAIR CITY OF LONDON.
(A Design for a Fresco in the New Houses of Parliament.)

Despite the evidence put forward by Snow, it was still widely believed that cholera was an airborne disease until, in 1883, Robert Koch isolated the bacterium which causes cholera. The last cholera epidemic was in 1866, and the eventual recognition of it as a water-borne disease did much to prevent further outbreaks.

Parliament published the Public Health Act in 1875 making it compulsory for all town councils to build and maintain effective sewers and water systems. This did much to improve the sanitary conditions in the large towns and cities where before, up to 200 people may have been sharing one toilet.

In **developed** countries today, diseases such as typhoid and cholera are rare. There were only seven suspected cases of cholera in Britain in 1986 and no confirmed cases, and 124 cases of typhoid fever. It is estimated that 85% of these are contracted abroad. However, in under-developed countries, the lack of a good, constant supply of fresh drinking water remains a real problem. This can lead to food contamination, as food is often prepared using the water.

WHAT YOU CAN DO

1 Study John Snow's map. How many houses were there where people died?

2 How else may people have caught cholera in the Broad Street region of London?

3 Write a brief imaginative passage about life in an overcrowded city street.

It is estimated that 1500 million inhabitants of the Third World have no access to safe water supplies and eight out of every ten diseases are caused by unclean water.

Claw dam, Zimbabwe.

There have been many large-scale schemes such as dams, hydro-electric power stations and complicated **irrigation** works which have provided regions with water for agriculture as well as for domestic use. These rely heavily on modern technology which needs money and considerable expertise to be maintained. These schemes may be funded by developed nations, often as part of trade deals and work contracts.

Large projects often produce abundant supplies of water. This can encourage the farmers to produce crops which need more water than those traditionally grown in the climate. This increases the demand for water still further. Some of the water is wasted because of inadequate drainage and evaporation.

Charities such as Oxfam concentrate more on smaller projects which, whilst less ambitious, are easily maintained by the technology already available in the developing countries.

Many small settlements rely on communal wells for their water. Carrying water is a time-consuming task which takes a lot of energy. A family consisting of mother, father and five children needs 40 litres of water a day just to survive, and 200 litres if they are to keep clean and healthy.

Oxfam produces leaflets giving practical advice to developing countries on water sanitation, filtration, storage, etc.

Oxfam Water Supply Scheme

WATER DISTRIBU PACK

OXFAM/DELAGUA WATER TESTING KIT

Information on the purpose and use of the Water Testing Kit, an essential part of OXFAM's Water Supply Scheme for emergencies and long term use.

Natural disasters can also lead to outbreaks and epidemics of food- and water-borne diseases. This is because any earth movement tends to fracture water and sewage pipes, causing contamination of water supplies. Flooding in built-up areas can lead to the sewerage systems overflowing causing foul water to run through streets and houses.

Modern technology has led to some diseases being spread through humidifiers and cooling towers which are part of air-conditioning systems. Several outbreaks of the very dangerous Legionnaire's disease have been attributed to inhaling tiny contaminated droplets from these sources of water.

Recent flooding in the UK (above) and in Bangladesh (below).

Problems occur when the communal wells become contaminated with sewage, so a simple preventive measure is to ensure that the well shaft is lined with stones or concrete which stops pollutants moving through from the neighbouring soil. Another effective way of avoiding contamination is the safe disposal of sewage in pit **latrines** which are well away from water supplies. Mechanical pumps can also pump water more efficiently, thus saving energy.

WHAT YOU CAN DO

1 If you had a substantial amount of money to spend helping a country to provide a safer drinking water system, would you go for a large irrigation scheme, or concentrate on smaller projects? Write down the pros and cons for each option.

2 If a person can carry 15 litres of water comfortably in one trip, how many trips will they have to make in a day to provide enough water for a family to stay clean and healthy?

3 Food poisoning

Unlike food- and water-borne diseases, food poisoning is caused by eating contaminated food which contains harmful numbers of food poisoning microbes. It is either the toxins made by the microbes or the microbes themselves which cause us to be ill.

Bacteria are microscopic, single-celled living organisms. They are found nearly everywhere in the world, and many of them are completely harmless to us. We actually use the action of bacteria to produce substances that are useful to mankind. This is called **biotechnology**. Bacteria are used in cheese and yoghurt making. It is a very small proportion of them which are harmful or **pathogenic**.

Bacteria reproduce by **binary fission**. If the conditions are right, they will divide in two. This means that in a short time, there can be a very large number of bacteria. If one bacterium of the length 3μm ($^3/_{1\,000\,000}$ of a metre) divides every twenty minutes, it will form a colony the size of a pinhead in nine hours, which will contain over 100 million bacteria. As this colony is barely visible, it would not necessarily be spotted on food before eating, and in some cases, one million bacteria would be enough to make you ill.

Fungi are another group of microbes which have many uses. The baking and brewing industries use yeast extensively. We eat mushrooms and other species of fungus. There is a small proportion of fungi which can cause illness, including food poisoning.

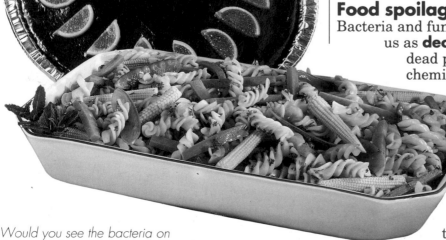

Would you see the bacteria on these meals?

A bacterium

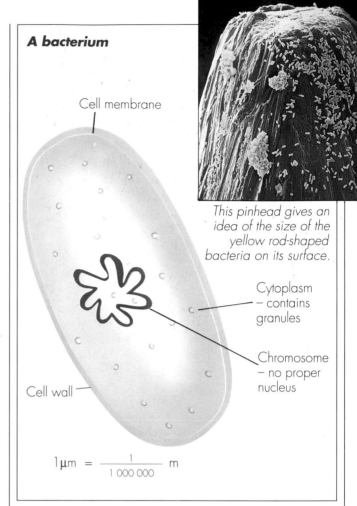

This pinhead gives an idea of the size of the yellow rod-shaped bacteria on its surface.

Cell membrane

Cytoplasm – contains granules

Chromosome – no proper nucleus

Cell wall

$$1\,\mu m = \frac{1}{1\,000\,000}\ m$$

WHAT YOU CAN DO

1 Calculate how many bacteria of size 5 μm × 1 μm would be needed to fill a rectangle 1 mm × 5 mm.

2 If one bacterium divided every half an hour, how long would it take for the colony to fill the rectangle?

Food spoilage organisms
Bacteria and fungi are of great importance to us as **decomposers**. They break down dead plants and animals into simple chemicals to enable a new generation of plants to gain the raw materials needed for healthy growth. This recycling is essential for supporting all life on Earth. Our problem is that we do not want these microbes to start to colonise the plant and animal substances we need for food.

15

Mushrooms – commonly encountered edible fungi.

Obviously decaying food (left) and what appears to be safe-looking food, but which could be contaminated with disease-causing organisms (right).

Different bacteria and fungi will colonise the decaying food at different times, depending on which food group they live on. They are described as saprophytic, that is, they obtain their nutrients from dead and decaying plants or animals. Food in an advanced state of **decay** is obvious not only from its appearance but also its smell which is caused by the waste products of the microbial action.

Nobody would eat food which looks and smells terrible, but sometimes food can be contaminated with pathogenic organisms and smell and taste perfectly normal.

It is the pathogenic bacteria which we must try to avoid. Food poisoning bacteria are those which find their way in varying quantities onto our food. If they are left in favourable conditions, they will multiply and reach a dangerous level.

WHAT YOU CAN DO

1 Which food poisoning bacteria can be found in soil?

2 *Salmonella* is found in which foods?

3 What is the organism responsible for causing botulism?

4 Which four microbes may be found in meat dishes?

5 Why might *Bacillus cereus* poison be difficult to avoid?

TYPE OF FOOD POISONING	BACTERIA	SOURCE
Salmonella	The *Salmonella* group of bacteria (many species)	Raw meat, eggs, poultry.
Campylobacter	The *Campylobacter* group of bacteria (several species)	Poultry, raw milk, water.
Listeria	*Listeria monocytogenes*	Soil, manure, water. Cook-chill foods, soft cheeses, chicken, pâté, prepared salads, chilled processed foods.
Bacillus cereus	*Bacillus cereus*	Found in most places. Fried rice.
Botulism	*Clostridium botulinum*	Soil, vegetables, fish, meat.
Clostridium perfringens	*Clostridium perfringens*	Intestines, including man. Meat dishes, food with low oxygen content. Soil and dust.
Staphylococcal	*Staphylococcus aureus*	Skin, nose, boils, cuts.

The bacteria which cause food poisoning.

How do the bacteria get onto food?

Raw meats, fish and poultry contain a large number of bacteria which were present in the gut of the animal. During the slaughtering of the animal, these bacteria will be transferred onto the meat. *Salmonella* lives in the guts of a large number of chickens, and some of the bacteria are left in the carcase of the chicken. Careful cooking will destroy these bacteria, but it is essential that raw chicken should not be allowed to come into contact with other foods.

Vegetables which are grown in soil will contain many soil microbes on their surfaces, some of which can be harmful. Bringing dirty shoes and boots and unwashed vegetables into a kitchen will also bring in these microbes. All other vegetables and fruits will have a number of bacteria on their surfaces. Because of this, they should always be thoroughly washed in cold water before being eaten.

Pressure cooking is a particularly effective way of cooking because it raises the temperature of the food to well above 100°C which is effective in killing bacterial **spores** as well as bacteria.

There are microbes all around us. Airborne microbes can settle onto uncovered food. Washing food with water from an unreliable source can also pass on microbes.

One of the main ways in which food is contaminated is by **vectors**. Vectors are living things which move the microbes from one source of infection to another, often without being affected by the infection themselves. We are obvious vectors, and often pass on microbes to others when we do not observe hygiene guidelines.

Another vector is the housefly. The housefly feeds on most organic matter, including animal faeces and compost heaps as well as our food. It carries the microbes on its hairy body and legs, and also in its digestive system. Flies feed by releasing digestive juices through their mouthpieces onto the food source. The food is then digested and sucked up in a soluble form. This means that the microbes from the fly's last feeding place will be squirted onto the food with the digestive juices, thus spreading infections.

Other vectors of disease and infection are pests such as insects and **vermin**. Signs of **infestation** to look for include the sight of animal droppings, chewed packaging and/or the presence of insects in dry foods.

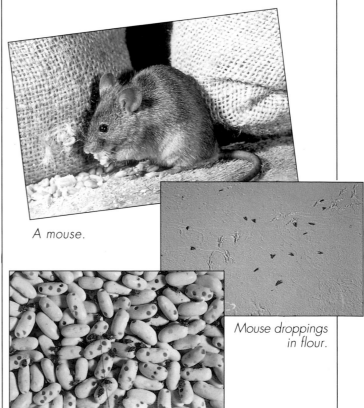

A mouse.

Mouse droppings in flour.

Beans infested with bean weevils.

17

The control of pests

Insects

Insect **pests** include houseflies, ants, wasps, mites and cockroaches. They eat a varied diet which includes most of what we eat. Whilst they eat, they pass on microbes which they have picked up from other food sources such as animal faeces, rotting animal carcases and rubbish. To prevent insects from overrunning premises, you must stop them from entering and getting to the food, make sure that you do not provide any breeding grounds in or immediately outside your kitchen and kill the insects at some stage in their life cycle.

A female bluebottle laying her eggs on the surface of a piece of raw meat left exposed in the kitchen.

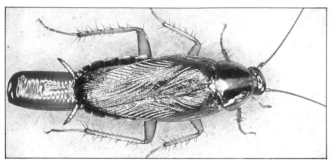

A cockroach.

Signs of insect infestation include larvae, eggs or even live or dead adult insects found in food.

Flying insects can be killed using an ultraviolet fly trap which attracts the insects onto an electrified grid. These are often used in food shops. Wire screens over windows can stop insects from entering. Fly spray can also be used, but care must be taken in kitchens as they must not be sprayed near food. Regular cleaning of kitchens will avoid food debris being left as an appetising meal for crawling insects such as cockroaches and ants. Damp, dark places like under the sink or between kitchen units should be regularly cleaned and checked for signs of cockroaches.

Rats and mice

Rats and mice can carry many pathogenic microbes. Signs of vermin infestation include droppings, gnawed packets, holes under fences and doors, even footprints and marks on a kitchen floor.

Life cycle of the housefly.

To avoid infestation, there should be no holes leading from the outside into the kitchen or from cellars or where water or gas pipes enter the house. Kitchen refuse should be kept in gnaw-proof bins.

If the house is infested, you should contact your local council offices which will recommend a specialist pest controller. Rats and mice can be poisoned or trapped. As rat poison is also poisonous to humans, it is a job best left to experts, especially in food preparation areas.

WHAT YOU CAN DO

1 Which stage of the fly's life cycle would these methods affect?
a) Insecticide spray;
b) Covering foodstuffs;
c) Keeping manure heaps away from houses?

2 Look at the life cycle of the housefly. Think of three different ways that you could prevent the flies from a) reproducing; b) infesting your house.

3 Design a restaurant with a kitchen which is vermin-proof.

4 Household pets are often regarded as perfectly clean and harmless. They too can spread infections and should be kept well away from food and food preparation areas. Is it safe to let your dog lick your plate clean? Explain your answer.

Our body's response to disease

Our **immune system** can destroy a small number of invading microbes in the body, but is unable to deal with large numbers. We have cells called phagocytes, a type of white blood cell, which are able to engulf and digest foreign bodies. If the number of invaders is small, then they will all be destroyed and will do the body no harm.

If there are too many microbes for the phagocytes to destroy, then substances called **antigens** on the microbes will stimulate the body to produce

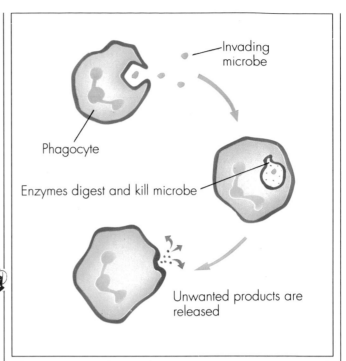

Phagocytosis. When a phagocyte comes into contact with a germ, it engulfs it. The germ is then killed and digested.

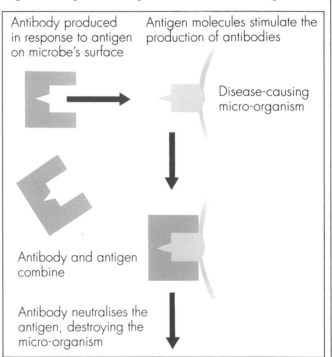

Antibodies in action.

antibodies. These are specific to the disease-causing organism and latch on to the organism, making them harmless. Vaccines work by giving us a very weak dose of a disease-causing organism or part of the organism which stimulates our bodies to make antibodies so we are immune to the disease. If we have the 'blueprint' already, it means that if we are invaded by the same type of organism again, we can produce antibodies very quickly. The first time a number of microbes invade, there will be a period of two weeks during which the antibodies are made.

Obviously, it is best if you do not get infected in the first place. To do this, the bacterial level in the food we eat and drink must be kept as low as possible. One way of doing this is to prevent the bacteria from multiplying to a dangerous level by ensuring that the conditions for their reproduction are unfavourable.

When do the bacteria become dangerous?

Favourable conditions for food-poisoning bacteria vary, since different bacteria like slightly different conditions. In general though, bacteria need moisture, a plentiful supply of nutrients and warmth in order to multiply.

Temperature

Most bacteria reproduce quickest in warm temperatures. The cooler the temperature the slower the reproduction. If the temperature is high – at least above 70°C – then most of the bacteria will be killed. There are some, the thermophilic bacteria, which prefer temperatures between 45°C and 75°C. The *Listeria* bacterium is able to multiply at low temperatures – even at the temperature of most fridges. Some have been observed reproducing at temperatures as low as –5°C.

The effects of heat on bacteria.

Moisture

Bacteria need moisture to reproduce. If the conditions are dry, then most bacteria will become inactive.

In unfavourable conditions, bacteria can produce spores called **endospores**. These are a way of protecting the bacteria, to enable it to continue reproducing when conditions become more favourable. These spores can withstand drying, **disinfectants** and a greater degree of heat than the bacteria themselves. These spores are the most resistant living things known. Some need a temperature of over 120°C for five minutes to kill them.

Oxygen

The bacterium causing botulism, *Clostridium botulinum*, is found everywhere. This is an example of an **anaerobic** bacterium – preferring an environment with little or no oxygen. In normal food preparation, the bacteria will be killed, but the spores are very heat resistant and could still be present. If they are in conditions where there is little oxygen, such as in the middle of a cooked dish, or in a can, the spores will germinate into a normal bacterial cell, which will then start to multiply and produce toxins, with the result that the food will cause food poisoning.

Other bacteria need a plentiful supply of oxygen before they can divide, ie they are **aerobic**.

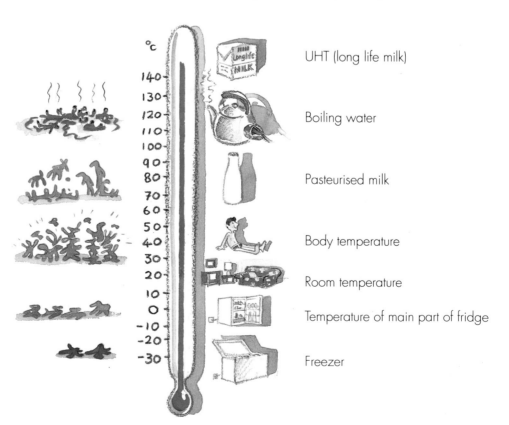

°C	
140	UHT (long life milk)
130	
120	Boiling water
110	
100	
90	
80	Pasteurised milk
70	
60	
50	
40	Body temperature
30	
20	Room temperature
10	
0	Temperature of main part of fridge
–10	
–20	Freezer
–30	

pH

Bacteria will multiply best at a certain pH. Most bacteria prefer a pH of between 6.8 and 7.2. If the conditions are of a different acidity to the one preferred by the microbe, growth and reproduction will be slowed down. In extreme conditions (very acid or alkaline), reproduction of the majority of microbes will stop completely. There are some exceptions. *Vibrio cholerae*, which causes the disease cholera, can multiply in very alkaline conditions.

WHAT YOU CAN DO

It is possible to make yoghurt by pouring sterilised milk into a container, adding a dessert spoon of natural live yoghurt to it, and leaving it at about 40°C for approximately eight hours. Every implement used must be cleaned thoroughly before use by scalding with boiling water to kill unwanted microbes.

Design experiments to see how temperature effects the action of the yoghurt bacteria by preparing yoghurt cultures and leaving them in different conditions.

How might you test the effect of pH?

High risk foods

Foods that are more likely to cause food poisoning are those which have been left for long periods of time in conditions favourable for bacterial growth. Liquid foods such as soups, stocks, sauces and gravy are ideal for rapid microbial growth so should never be kept and reheated. Shellfish are also high risk because of the way that they feed. If they have been in contaminated waters, any toxin will be concentrated inside the shellfish as it filters litres of water to obtain nutrients. Dishes made with cream are high risk, as are dishes made with raw or lightly cooked eggs. Any raw or undercooked meat or poultry is also best avoided.

Bad practices

Leaving hot food to cool for longer than 1½ hours provides the optimum temperature for microbial growth. Food should be cooled quickly, covered and then refrigerated if it is not to be eaten immediately. Never attempt to cool the food by putting it straight in the fridge. This warms up the fridge to an unacceptable level.

If you use a microwave, make sure the food is thoroughly cooked. Follow the manufacturers' recommendations about heating times and standing times. Microwaves cook from the outside in, and if you do not leave the cooked food to stand for long enough, the heat cannot conduct through the food to produce an even temperature.

Reheating food dishes over and over again is a very bad practice. Food should be reheated once only. If the dish still has not been finished, throw out the left-overs. Every time you heat anything, it increases the length of time it is at the right temperature for microbial growth.

Food which is to be reheated should be heated thoroughly so all of it is hot. If it is only warmed through, parts of the food will not reach 70°C and so some bacteria will remain. This includes **cook-chill** food – ready-made dishes found in cold cabinets in supermarkets which only require reheating.

Pouring hot sauces and gravy on platters of cold meats before serving can warm the meat to the dangerous temperature, whilst the moisture in the gravy helps to provide ideal conditions for microbes. If you want to serve gravy, make sure it is very hot and served separately. Never keep left-over gravy or milk sauces. They are ideal food for microbes.

Storing cooked food next to raw food and cheeses is also bad practice. The heating will have destroyed most microbes on the food, but microbes can be passed on by contact from badly wrapped food introducing new microbes to the cooked food.

Eating raw fruit and vegetables without washing them first can be dangerous. **Pesticide residues**, soil microbes and microbes passed on from handlers could be present on the food.

Always wash the food in water from a mains supply or boiled or bottled water if mains water is not available.

The government's Chief Medical Officer put forward the following recommendations following the salmonella and listeria scares in 1989:

● Do not eat raw eggs or uncooked foods made with them.
● It is advisable that vulnerable people such as the elderly, the sick, pregnant women and babies should only consume eggs which have been cooked until the white and yolk are solid.
● Pregnant women and those patients with a low resistance to infection should avoid eating certain types of soft cheeses and should thoroughly reheat cook-chill meals and ready-to-eat poultry rather than eat them cold.

It was added that as long as the public followed general hygiene practices, there should be no need for us to change the type of food we regularly eat and enjoy.

How dangerous is food poisoning?
It may seem that it is impossible to avoid food poisoning and that there is a major risk to our health every time we pick up a fork. In comparative terms, the risk is still very small.

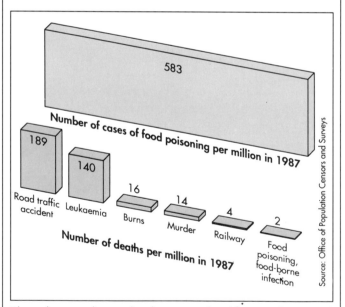

The relative risks involved in everyday life. Food poisoning is, at best, unpleasant, and if you are already ill or weak, elderly or very young, it can be fatal.

WHAT YOU CAN DO

Design a universal sign/poster warning of the danger of reheating food more than once. It should not have any words so that it does not rely on kitchen employees understanding English.

4 Food preservation

Food **preservation** has been used for centuries to keep food in an edible state for as long as possible. This was very important when food was harvested and stored in an attempt to have sufficient for when conditions were not favourable for plant growth. Animals were slaughtered as there was not enough food for them through the winter, with only breeding stock retained for the following year.

To preserve food, you need to make the conditions unfavourable for bacterial growth, so that food-spoilage bacteria and food-poisoning bacteria will not affect it, and it can be kept for a longer time.

To understand how food preservation works, it is necessary to look at the conditions bacteria need to reproduce. These are:

> The correct temperature
> The optimum pH
> Moisture
> Nutrients

Preservation works by taking away or altering these conditions or by destroying all the microbes present.

Traditional methods of food preservation

The oldest methods of food preservation are salting, pickling, drying, heating, smoking and jamming.

Salting
Salting reduces the amount of water present in the food, by the process of **osmosis**. Water will move to areas with a very high salt concentration, so a large quantity of salt rubbed into the food, or dissolved in water as brine (in which the food is immersed) will draw the water out of the food, making the conditions unfavourable for microbes. This obviously affects the taste of the food considerably. Bacon and fish are often salted.

Pickling
Some foods are pickled in brine, others are pickled in vinegar. Vinegar creates a very acid environment which is unsuitable for bacterial growth. Onions and other vegetables are preserved like this. The vegetables have a very characteristic flavour.

Sun-dried fruit.

Drying
Drying is a method which is widely used for foods such as fruit, vegetables and some meats. This used to be carried out by leaving the fruits in the sun to dry. Sultanas and raisins were produced using this method for thousands of years. Although the microbes present will not be destroyed by the drying process, deprived of water they will be unable to reproduce. The texture of dried food is changed considerably.

Sides of salmon being smoked.

Smoking

Traditionally, the food is hung in special chambers and is exposed to smoke created by burning wood or peat. A deposit of smoke residue is left over the surface of the food which it then preserves. Smoking preserves food because the smoke residue is high in nitrites and nitrates which are toxic to most microbes. Some methods of smoking involve the food being heated and dried which also kills the microbes. Like salting, this leaves a characteristic taste and smell to the food and is usually used in conjunction with salting. This process is often lengthy and is not used very much nowadays. Foods such as smoked salmon are regarded as a delicacy, with the smoky taste and smell being considered assets.

Some 'smoked' food such as fish is treated by dipping it into a liquid which imparts the flavour of the smoke and also dyes it a distinct colour. This is a legal practice and the product can be described as smoked fish, despite not having gone through any smoking process.

Jamming/bottling

If there is a high concentration of sugar present, bacteria are unable to grow. Again, this is because osmosis occurs, causing the bacteria to lose water to the strong concentration of the syrup. If fruit is mixed with a large amount of sugar and heated, it will be preserved for some time. Some moulds can live on jams, which is why they should be sealed promptly after being put in clean, sterilised jars. Obviously, the sugar alters the taste of the fruit, making it far sweeter.

Heat treatment

Food which has been cooked (heated right through) for long enough will keep for longer as all the microbes present will be destroyed. Unless the food is then refrigerated or sealed, airborne microbes will contaminate it and it will start to spoil.

Canning

Canning, as a method of food preservation, has been in existence for over 100 years. It was used as far back as 1806 by the French Navy as a means of keeping a food supply on ships. Food is canned, then heated to sterilise the contents. It is sealed so that there will be no microbial contamination from the outside. As the food is effectively cooked by this heating process, the taste and texture of the food will be different from that of fresh food. Canned food will last for a long time, and it is rare that canned food causes food poisoning. Some anaerobic bacteria, for example those which cause botulism, can reproduce in the conditions inside the can.

CASE STUDY

The Aberdeen typhoid outbreak, 1964

On Tuesday, 19 May 1964, two students were admitted to hospital with suspected typhoid fever. There was already a family of four in the hospital suffering from what was first diagnosed as gastro-enteritis. During the next few days, a boy and then the rest of his family were also admitted, and this was followed by another family being admitted on 20 May.

In all, 487 people were admitted to hospital. Most of these people were diagnosed as suffering from typhoid fever although a small number were later found not to have it.

When corned beef is manufactured, fresh chilled meat enters a factory, is processed and then canned. The cans are heated up, and then rapidly cooled. This is often done by submerging the cans in water, which may not come from a wholesome source. The cans are then put in boxes and sent all over the world, usually by sea. There is a period of incubation, when the cans are stored by the manufacturers for a length of time so that if any are contaminated, they will 'blow' (ie bowed out at the ends), because there will be a large build-up of gas inside.

It is likely that the typhoid bacillus entered a damaged can as it was being cooled by river water. Subsequent tests showed that in large (6 lb) cans, bacteria can thrive without producing a detectable quantity of gas, so the bacilli could have multiplied to dangerous levels without affecting the appearance of the can. The bacteria would be able to multiply rapidly once the can was open. The infected can was sold in a supermarket between 7 and 9 May 1964. There was probably contamination of other cooked meats from the infected corned beef at the supermarket, although the shop was found to be well managed and clean. The meat was also sliced on demand using one of two meat slicers or a knife which was wiped with a disinfected cloth periodically. The staff were clean, but handled the large cuts of meat when slicing the food.

INSIDE THE CITY OF FEAR

New warning – and visitors are told to stay away

ABERDEEN was in the grip of fear last night as the typhoid toll continued to rise.

At tea time last night, 199 p were in hospital 44 being sus cases.

As people were warned come to Aberdeen for the ne weeks and local folk were adv stay at home the town won "the beleaguered city" from Officer Dr. Ian McQueen.

Quarter million people at risk

ABERDEEN is now a beleaguered city. That was the description of it given today by Dr Ian A. G. MacQueen, City medical officer of health, as he made a dramatic appeal for action to stem the second major wave of typhoid. His advice was:

● DON'T leave the city if you Aberdonian.

rdeen
ly

TYPHOID: MASS JABS READY

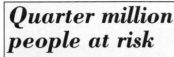

A MASTER plan is now ready to aid typhoid-stricken Aberdeen if the call goes out...

Last night as the toll soared it was announced by the Scottish Home and Health Department that

Preliminary investigations showed that many of the patients had a common milk supplier. This was investigated and the tests for the typhoid bacillus proved negative. The water supply was also checked. It was also suggested that this outbreak could be caused by a carrier of the typhoid infection. The staff of the supermarket where most of the patients shopped were all tested for the disease. No staff member was carrying the disease although six members of staff contracted the disease later. It is fairly certain that they were contaminated from the same source as the others.

It then came to light that many of the affected people had eaten cold meat bought from one supermarket. This was the only common food link. The cold meats and their countries of origin were investigated. The typhoid bacillus was type 34 which is found in Spain and South America. The supermarket did not stock any Spanish canned meat, so the investigation centred on South American meats – in particular some Argentinian corned beef.

WHAT YOU CAN DO

1 At what stage in the manufacturing process did contamination take place?

2 Not all of the patients who contracted typhoid ate corned beef. List the ways that they could have contracted the disease.

3 Using the information in chapter 2, list the symptoms of typhoid.

Modern methods of food preservation

Refrigeration

Most microbes become inactive at low temperatures and, because the enzymes which control their life processes slow down considerably as the temperature drops, they stop reproducing. Chilling food will not kill the microbes, so when the food warms up, the microbes will start to reproduce again if the conditions are right.

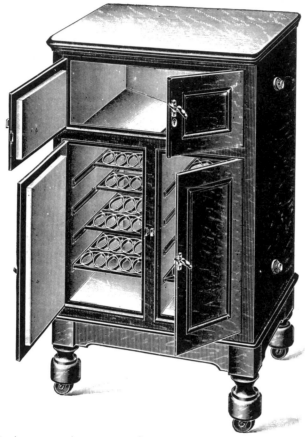

Early twentieth-century refrigerator.

Before the days of refrigerators, people used cool pantries and cellars to store food in an attempt to keep it in good condition for longer, and for centuries Eskimos have preserved food by burying it in ice. Large households used to keep ice houses for storing food. Modern-day refrigerators, which keep the food at between 0°C and 3°C, should be used to store many foods to prevent microbial growth.

Freezing

Microbes are not destroyed by freezing. As with refrigeration, at the low temperatures found in domestic freezers (–17°C to –23°C) microbes become inactive and are unable to reproduce. The water in the food is frozen into ice, so the bacteria are also deprived of moisture. This

stops any deterioration but again, as soon as the food warms up, the bacteria become active and will start to reproduce.

It was not until the 1920s that quick freezing was developed to preserve food. Food has to be frozen quickly so that the ice crystals which form are kept small and do not destroy the texture of the food.

Industrially, food is frozen by passing it through a tunnel of very cold air or by placing it on a very cold surface.

Freeze drying

In freeze drying, the food is frozen, and the ice is then drawn off into a vacuum. This removes all the moisture and is a very effective method of food preservation as long as the food is kept dry and in a sealed container. Dried foods such as coffee, custard powder, powdered milk, soups and even peas are preserved by this method.

Frozen food coldroom with heavy-duty equipment for fast freezing.

Chemical preservatives

Preservatives have been defined as substances which inhibit the growth of microbes, or mask signs of the effect of these microbes.

Food can be preserved by adding chemicals which are toxic to microbes. Hops were originally added to beer to preserve it, and wine used to be fortified with spirits (distilled alcohol) to stop the bacteria present in it from turning it into vinegar.

A total of 83 'E' numbers have been given to preservatives. There are about 35 principal food preservatives in use today. These include:

Sulphur dioxide – this is used to preserve fruit. It is added during jam making and used in wine making. It is driven off during the manufacturing process. Used in Roman times!

Nitrites and Nitrates – traditionally smoked and cured meats have high levels of nitrites which are toxic to bacteria, especially those responsible for botulism.

Hyperactive behaviour in children and food allergies have been linked to food additives. The Hyperactive Children's Support Group has a list of chemical additives which it recommends should be excluded from the diets of hyperactive children. Eighteen preservatives are on that list.

INGREDIENTS:
Skimmed milk, Vegetable oil, Hydrogenated vegetable oil, Buttermilk, Caseinates, Salt, Acidity regulators (E325, E331, E339), Emulsifier (E471), Preservative (E202), Flavouring, Vitamins A & D, Colour (E160a)

St Ivel, Hemyock, Devon

5021 6628

1 *'If preservatives are harmful to bacteria, what are they doing to us? Why can't we use other methods of food preservation?' Discuss this amongst your class.*

2 *It has been said that there is concern about only one in five of food additives used in Britain today. Maurice Hanssen, the author of 'E for additives' lists 19 preservatives which are either the most unnecessary or potentially worrying. What do you think the government and food manufacturers should do about it?*

WHAT YOU CAN DO

Look at some packaged foods. Identify those with preservatives ('E' numbers 200–283). Are there any similar foods which have not used preservatives?

Vacuum packing

Vacuum packing works by packaging the food in a plastic or foil container, from which the air is then drawn out. This stops any deterioration by microbes which need oxygen, but will not prevent the anaerobic bacteria from reproducing. Cured meats and some uncooked meats are preserved in this way although the product should be refrigerated. At temperatures of 1–2°C vacuum packed meat can be kept for two months.

Ohmic heating

During ohmic heating, the food is heated by putting an electric current through it during manufacture. The food offers an electrical resistance to the current and therefore becomes hot. This takes about 90 seconds and is used on a continuous production line. It is used mainly for liquid foods and it cooks the food very quickly.

Sterilising

If food is heated to a high temperature for a considerable length of time, then it is likely that all the microbes present will be killed. Some foods are prepared, sterilised and packed in foil or plastic containers. They do not need to be chilled or frozen and unless the packaging gets damaged, the food will remain safe for a considerable time.

Milk can be sterilised by heating it for 30 minutes at 105°C, but this changes the flavour considerably so other methods are used to rid the raw milk of microbes.

Pasteurisation

It is mostly milk, cheese, canned ham and beer which are pasteurised. Pasteurisation involves heating the food up to 63°C for 30 minutes. Flash pasteurisation involves heating for 15 seconds at a temperature of 72°C. The taste of the product is altered very little, and the treatment destroys most microbes. It will not kill all spores however, so the food should always be kept refrigerated as well.

Ultra Heat Treatment (UHT)

Liquids such as fruit juices and milk are treated by being heated to 135°C for three seconds. The product is then sealed in sturdy cardboard containers. This method can preserve the food for some months. Because it has been sterilised, it need not be refrigerated unless the container has been opened. The taste of the food is changed very little.

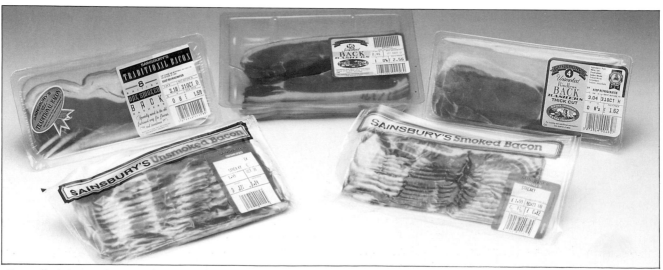

Controlled Atmosphere Packaging (CAP) – above – offers an alternative to air packs and vacuum packs – below. With CAP, a gas mixture is chosen to suit the product.

Milk can be preserved in a number of different ways.

Irradiation

Many airborne microbes are killed naturally by ultraviolet **irradiation** from the sun. Food irradiation involves exposing the food to γ (gamma) **radiation** from a radioactive source. This kills all living organisms so the food is not attacked by food-spoilage bacteria and keeps fresher for longer. It will not alter the appearance, taste or texture of the food. If X-rays are used, the food can be treated after it has been packed. Unlike other forms of food preservation which involve heat, irradiation will not affect naturally occurring chemicals called **enzymes**, although it will affect the vitamin content of the food as do many of the other conventional methods of food preservation. Enzymes change the texture of fruit and cause meat to become tender, so γ radiation will not stop the natural changes like ripening from occurring.

Twenty-four hours must elapse before food that has been irradiated can be placed on the shelves.

Irradiation of certain foods was permitted in the United Kingdom from January 1991. Regulations control the amount of radiation that can be used and the proper labelling of the food.

Irradiation prevents spoilage of strawberries (above).
Left – non-irradiated; right – irradiated.
Irradiation also prevents sprouting of onions (below).
Left – non-irradiated; right – irradiated.

29

PAUSE FOR THOUGHT

Concern has been voiced over food irradiation. Here are some of the common arguments for and against irradiation.

Sort these into arguments 'for' and 'against'. Try to research into this issue in more detail.

'The food is bound to be slightly radioactive, and what about possible changes in the chemicals in food which we may not know about?'

'If we've probably eaten irradiated food, then it obviously isn't harmful.'

'There are too many sources of radioactivity at the moment without *us* adding to them.'

'If this is done on a production line, how are we so sure that all the food has been treated enough to kill all the potentially harmful bacteria?'

'If other countries are allowing it, their scientists must have passed it as safe.'

'There are many more natural ways of preserving food without needing to use a method which has not been proved 100% safe.'

'Because it looks OK, we may forget to take sensible hygiene precautions and forget that the food could be contaminated after being irradiated so it should not be used.'

'As it is the toxins from bacteria that make us ill, irradiation will not have any effect on them, so we still need to be careful about what we eat.'

'If irradiation helps to keep food for longer, then it should be used. We can't afford, as a country, to allow food to go to waste.'

WHAT YOU CAN DO

1 Conduct a survey to find out how many people know what irradiation is.

2 a) Either at home or in a room which is suitable, eg a home economics room, conduct a taste and smell test on your friends using the following types of milk:
  i)   UHT
  ii) Pasteurised
  iii) Dried, reconstituted
  iv) Sterilised
  v)   Canned (evaporated).
b) Which were easiest to guess? Which methods of preservation changed the taste most? Least? Compare the prices of the milk per pint.
c) Try the same test with another food which is preserved in different ways, eg garden peas.
d) How do the methods of preservation alter the colour and texture?
e) Which is the cheapest type of milk per 100g?

DO NOT CONDUCT THIS EXPERIMENT IN A SCIENCE LABORATORY. IT IS UNSAFE TO EAT OR DRINK ANYTHING IN LABORATORIES.

5 Food hygiene from farm to food shop

On the farm

Crops

Modern intensive farming often relies heavily on **chemical fertilisers** to provide the crops with the nutrients they want. Pesticides are applied to the crop to prevent the crop being spoiled by insects and other animal pests. Unless these chemicals are removed from the crop by washing, they can cause food poisoning or allergic reactions. Similarly, fungicides and general pesticides which are used to prevent stored grain from going mouldy and deteriorating must be removed carefully before the grain is further processed.

Most grain which is harvested for milling does not have a high concentration of pesticides. Some problems have arisen when grain which is selected for seeding is accidentally mistaken for food grain. Seeding grain is often treated to prevent spoiling over the winter and stored in silos on the farm. In this case, mistaken identity can cause contamination of the flour.

Meat and meat products

Close checks are made on animals which are raised for meat. Vets make regular checks on the animals' health by testing for various diseases, eg tuberculin-testing of cattle.

The conditions in which dairy cattle are kept are also closely monitored. Milking parlours should be clean and free from excrement. They should be easy to clean, and all the milking machinery should be sterilised with **disinfectant** solution to avoid any cross-contamination of the raw milk. Similarly, tankers used for transporting milk should be spotlessly clean. Regular testing of raw milk makes sure that it is free from infectious bacteria such as species of *Brucella*.

Farmyard management is also important. Manure heaps should be kept away from any housing areas and covered so that houseflies cannot breed in them.

The production line

Grain is taken to commercial mills for milling. Samples of each lorry-load are checked for quality (gluten and carbohydrate content) and for signs of disease. If the lorry-load is substandard, it will be rejected. The grain is stored in silos before being milled. It is then sieved to remove stones, twigs, hard/dry grains and other foreign objects before milling. Sometimes the flour will be bleached with a bleaching agent before being packed. The flour is then tested to check for any remaining impurities such as straw, insect cuticle or grit. If a certain quantity is found, the flour will be rejected.

During the period 1986–87, over 22 million cattle, calves, sheep and pigs were slaughtered in the UK for human consumption. Animals bred for food are taken to abattoirs or slaughterhouses to be humanely slaughtered. This is carefully monitored to ensure that suffering is minimal and that strict standards of hygiene are maintained.

We have already seen that raw meat contains many microbes. It is the job of an experienced team of people headed by an Environmental Health Officer or an authorised meat inspector to inspect thoroughly each carcase for any sign of disease or abnormalities. About 23% of whole or part carcases are rejected on hygiene grounds. Meat that has been rejected is either fully sterilised and sold for animal feeding stuff or fertiliser, or destroyed completely so that the diseased carcases do not remain a hazard to health.

Mad cow disease?

In May 1990, the government launched an emergency enquiry into a disease called **b**ovine **s**pongiform **e**ncephalopathy (BSE). The disease affects cattle and causes them to lose balance and co-ordination so that they are unsteady on their feet. As yet, it is not known which organism causes this disease, but it has been linked to a disease called scrapie, which affects sheep in much the same way. The disease causes little holes to appear in the brain tissue, making it look spongy.

One theory about how the cows have developed this disease is that they have been fed on animal feed made from the remains of sheep, including the brains, which have not been sterilised properly. If the sheep brains were infected, it could lead to a similar infection in cattle.

At present, there is no test to see if live cattle are infected. Only examination of the brain after slaughter of an animal showing all the symptoms tells the scientists that the animal was infected with BSE. It is being recommended that the brains and spinal cords of cows are not used with other **offal** for foodstuffs.

Scrapie has been recognised for over 200 years. As yet, no one has linked any human disease to scrapie. There is real concern that the organism causing BSE can cross from one species to another. Two cats died in May 1990, and an examination revealed that their brains had a similar appearance to that of a cow infected with BSE. It could be that the cats were infected from contaminated pet food, again made from infected animal remains. A human disease, Creutzfeldt-Jakob disease, which affects fewer than one in two million people per year, has similar symptoms to BSE.

Poultry is inspected at licensed poultry houses by a team of qualified inspectors, with veterinary surgeons and Environmental Health Officers overseeing this process. The conditions at the licensed places are covered by law. However, the regulations do not cover all poultry available to us. Two exceptions are poultry sold direct to the public or to retailers within a local area by poultry farmers. This means that there are chickens and other poultry being sold without any health checks at all. The salmonella scare in 1989, when it was announced by a government minister that most chicken flocks carried *Salmonella* bacteria, has made the public more aware of this, with the effect that some poultry farmers are voluntarily testing their flocks for

Salmonella infection. It is still essential to ensure that raw poultry is kept away from other foods, and cooked very thoroughly.

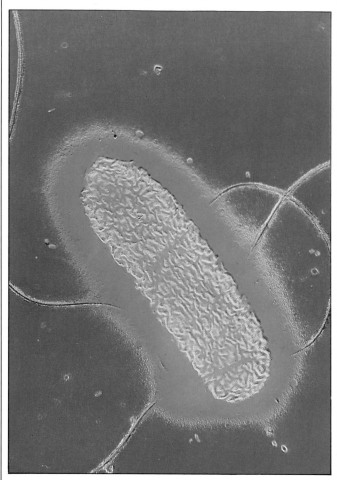

A Salmonella *bacterium.*

Reputable meat processors take a great deal of care when cooking, preparing and packaging meat products.

For work on the production line, managers look for staff with a strong sense of personal hygiene. When arriving for work, staff will put on suitable clothing which will be clean and made from easily washable fabric. It should either completely cover the handler's normal clothes, or ideally, be a complete change of clothing. Outdoor clothing and shoes will be stored in areas away from the food preparation area.

Before starting work, the food handlers thoroughly wash their hands and may even walk through a disinfectant foot bath to ensure that conditions are as sterile as possible.

Random samples of the food are taken throughout the manufacturing and packing process and sent to laboratories to check for microbial contamination. After processing and packaging, each pack will be individually checked to ensure that it is properly sealed.

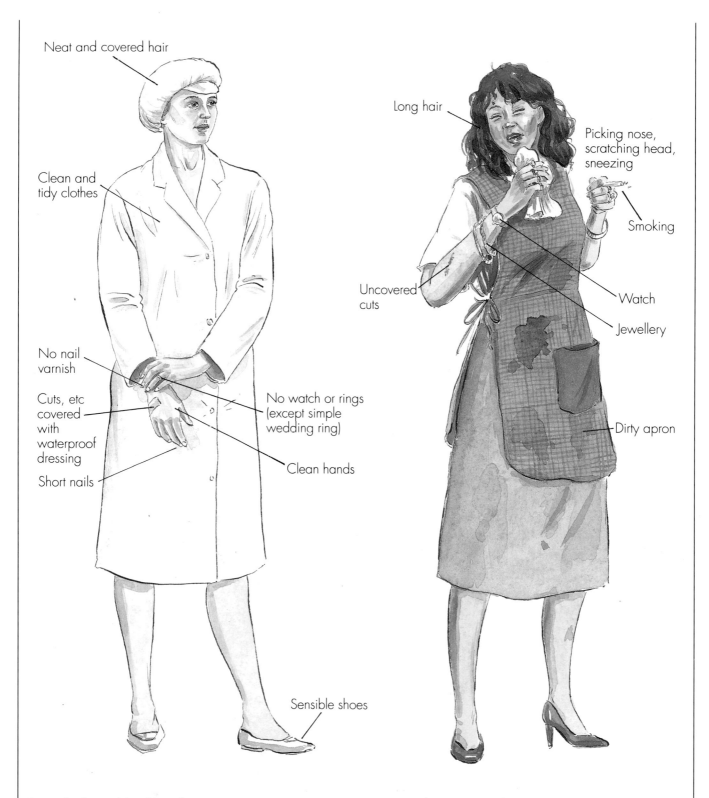

Neat and covered hair

Clean and tidy clothes

No nail varnish

Cuts, etc covered with waterproof dressing

Short nails

No watch or rings (except simple wedding ring)

Clean hands

Sensible shoes

Long hair

Picking nose, scratching head, sneezing

Smoking

Uncovered cuts

Watch

Jewellery

Dirty apron

Properly dressed food handler.

Would you employ someone like this?

Personal hygiene for food handlers

We have already seen what the well-dressed food handler should be wearing. Food handlers in factories, shops, restaurants, cafés – even hot dog stalls, must be very aware of their own personal habits and hygiene.

Hand-washing must be done properly. Rings (except simple wedding ring), watches and other hand jewellery should not be worn. Hands should be thoroughly washed, including between the fingers, the wrists and the forearms. Soap should be used, and a nail-brush if nails are dirty. For this reason, food handlers should not wear nail varnish as it is difficult to see if the nails are clean.

WHAT THE LAW SAYS

The Food Hygiene (General) Regulations, 1970

These state that food handlers must keep clean, cover cuts with waterproof dressings, wear suitable protective overclothing, must not smoke or spit and must report to the person managing the food business if they are suffering from food poisoning or a food-borne disease.

Food preparation areas should have a separate basin for washing hands, a good supply of disposable paper towels or an electric hand drier. A good, clean nail-brush and plenty of soap must also be provided.

It is against the law and contravenes building regulations to have a toilet leading directly off a kitchen. Toilet facilities should be provided well away from the main area, and notices reminding staff to wash their hands should be clearly posted.

Staff should be encouraged not to wear heavy make-up which can slough off, contaminating food. Long hair should be covered with a hat or tucked into a hairnet so that flakes of skin or hairs do not fall into the food. Strong-smelling perfume or aftershave (or even strong-smelling soap) can taint delicately flavoured food.

Staff should not smoke or eat whilst on duty. They should be permitted to do this when having regular rest breaks, and they must, of course, wash their hands again before resuming work.

Hands should be washed regularly and always after:

visiting the toilet

cleaning and disinfecting the kitchen

accidentally touching your face or neck (and in particular your nose, mouth, eyes and ears)

handling raw foods   handling rubbish

taste food with your fingers

lick your fingers

bite your nails

scratch your head

pick your nose

touch your face

pick your teeth

blow on food to cool it

sneeze or cough without a handkerchief

handle food unnecessarily

Staff illnesses

If food handlers have been ill with any disease, they should report this fact to their supervisor and stay off work until they have had their illness diagnosed and properly treated by a doctor. This is especially important if they have experienced vomiting and diarrhoea. This also applies to handlers if they have a sudden outbreak of spots or boils, as they can easily pass on the microbes causing the infection. If a food handler has been in contact with anyone with vomiting and diarrhoea, they should also inform their supervisor of this fact. It is the employer's legal responsibility to inform the local authority if any employee is suffering from food poisoning or a food-borne disease.

Workplaces should have a first-aid kit clearly labelled, containing waterproof dressings. All cuts and grazes should be covered with a blue waterproof dressing. The colour blue is used so that if the dressing does become detached, it is easily seen (how many blue foods can you think of?). Some blue plasters also contain a detectable metallic strip so that they would show up on in-line metal detection equipment. Any large absorbent dressing should be covered completely with a finger guard.

Transport

Food is transported from factories to warehouses or refrigeration units in delivery vehicles. These are regularly inspected by Environmental Health Officers to ensure that they are clean, that refrigerated containers are at the correct temperature and that they are not dirty or contaminated. Tankers used for the transport of milk and milk products must be carefully cleaned between deliveries.

Imported food is examined carefully at seaports and airports by Environmental Health Officers. They ensure that the food is in good condition, and does not contain any substance or additive which is against our food regulations.

Bad practice.
Fresh fish must be treated hygienically.

Shops

Shops have strict hygiene standards. They will have an efficient stock-check system and rarely order surplus food. They should check the shelves regularly, marking down food which is reaching its date limit. They should make sure that when they stack their shelves, they move the existing stock forward and place the new stocks at the back (this is called **stock rotation**). Raw foods should be kept away from cooked and ready-to-eat foods. Freezers and refrigerated cabinets should be regularly serviced and defrosted and their temperatures checked daily. If freezers are overstocked, then the food at the top may be above the recommended temperature, which is between –18°C and –23°C. Refrigerated cabinets should be at temperatures between 0°C and 5°C.

Fresh fish should be stored on ice or in a chilled cabinet. The cabinet should be designed so that the public cannot touch the fish or breathe over it. Smoked fish or shellfish, which are normally eaten without further preparation, should be kept separately.

Meat and meat products should be refrigerated, with cooked and raw meats kept separately.

Cook-chill meals must be checked when the shelves are stacked and any meals with damaged packaging should be discarded.

Eggs should be kept in a cool, dry place. If kept under refrigeration, the eggs will require a little more cooking than those not refrigerated.

Supermarkets ensure the food products on sale are correctly stored.

Eating places

Where food is on sale for consumption by others, great care must be taken in food preparation and serving.

Food should be bought from a reputable supplier, and delivered regularly. Food should be checked in by a responsible person, and stored correctly. All food should be stored off the ground, and stock should be rotated, with the oldest stock being used first. Food should be removed from surplus packaging. All surfaces should be cleaned regularly, and the floors should be kept clear of food debris. Debris encourages vermin such as mice and rats and insects such as cockroaches. If there are signs of infestation, reputable pest control firms should be brought in to deal with the problem.

Refuse disposal is also important. Bins should have well-fitting lids and be emptied regularly.

Where possible, food should be prepared just before it is served up. If food has to be prepared in advance, it should be cooled quickly under cover, then refrigerated as soon as possible, and definitely within 1½ hours. The food should then be reheated thoroughly. The use of thermometers will help to check that the food has reached a safe temperature all the way through.

If food is on display in a carvery, servery or canteen it must be kept at a temperature of above 63°C so that it is too hot for most microbes to multiply, and it is a pleasant temperature for eating! If the servery is selling salads and cold sweets, they should be kept in a cool cabinet at a low-enough temperature for microbial growth to be suspended.

A high pressure detergent spray helps to remove unwanted dirt.

What health hazards are present here?

6 Food hygiene and us

Safe buying

There are many laws to protect us, the consumers, against buying food which can harm us. Since 1984, it has been easier to monitor food and the contents of our recipes, with the introduction of The Food Labelling Regulations. The label not only tells us the contents in order of weight, it also gives a **'best before'** date, or **'use by'** date, which tells us how long food is expected to be at its best and safest. In the case of the food which, from a microbiological point of view, is highly perishable and could, after a short time, pose a danger to health, it has to carry a 'use by' date. This should be expressed as a day and date. Storage instructions should also be displayed.

Food which is not highly perishable and which has a shelf-life of up to 18 months, will carry a date giving a month and a year and the food will be best before the end of that month.

If the foods are expected to retain their properties for longer than 18 months, the date can be given as 'best before end' plus the year only.

When shopping, it is often best to visit shops which are popular as this will ensure a rapid turnover of stock.

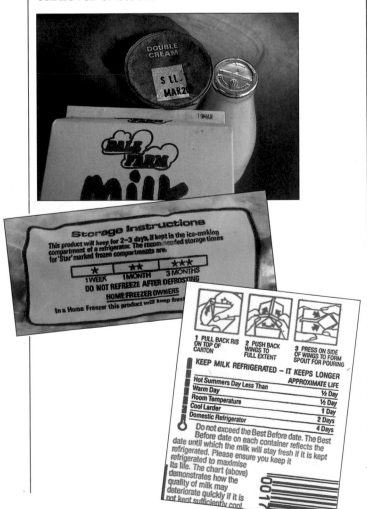

When buying food, check the following points:

● Does the shop look clean and well managed?

● Do the staff look clean and healthy?

● Are the freezers and cold storage units well stacked and not over-full?

● Is all unwrapped food handled with tongs or as little as possible, and is it covered or in a cabinet?

● Are raw and cooked meats kept separate?

● Are all packages secure and not split or damaged in any way?

● Has all pre-packed food got its 'use by' or 'best before' date clearly visible?

● Is all the food on shelves well clear of the floor and also well clear of the pavement or road?

● Are the tins and cans in good condition, not 'blown' (ie bowed out at the ends), dented or rusty?

WHAT YOU CAN DO

Visit a supermarket.

1 Make a list of foods which have a 'use by' date and a list of foods which have a 'best before' date.

2 Look in the cabinets. Is there any evidence of stock rotation? (Is the oldest stock at the front of the cabinet?)

Safe transporting

It is not a good idea to go food shopping, and then either leave the food in a car for the rest of the day or carry the food around with you whilst you finish the rest of the shopping. If you have bought any refrigerated or frozen items, they will start to warm up and any microbes present will start to multiply. If the foods thaw a lot, the quality will also be affected. It is best to shop for food at the end of a trip into town, or make a separate trip to do your food shopping.

When you buy a lot of food from a supermarket, it will save time and be safer if you take care packing the food efficiently before transporting it home. Ideally, frozen and refrigerated food, chilled foods and meat should be transported home in an insulated bag or cool box. If you do not have one, put all these goods in one bag, and if it will take more than a few minutes to transport them home, they can be insulated by wrapping them in newspaper. This will keep the food cooler, and if you keep frozen, refrigerated, tinned and dried foods in separate bags, it is also easier to unpack quickly once you get home. Perishable or easily damaged foods should, of course, be packed last and with great care.

Root vegetables should not come into contact with any cooked food or any other vegetable or fruit which may be eaten without further preparation.

Raw meat, meat products and shellfish should be wrapped and bagged up separately to avoid cross-contamination.

If you transport food home in a car, do not put the shopping right against a heater or on the back shelf on a sunny day.

Food storage in the home

The good food-storage practices which are encouraged in shops and commercial kitchens should also be followed at home. It is more efficient, less wasteful, and above all, safer. Where possible, vegetables should be stored in a cool, dry place off the ground, with root vegetables stored separately from others and in the dark.

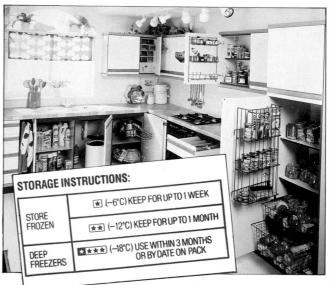

STORAGE INSTRUCTIONS:	
STORE FROZEN	★ (−6°C) KEEP FOR UP TO 1 WEEK
	★★ (−12°C) KEEP FOR UP TO 1 MONTH
DEEP FREEZERS	★★★ (−18°C) USE WITHIN 3 MONTHS OR BY DATE ON PACK

Dry goods should be stored in a cupboard, and once the package is open, the contents should be transferred to a dry, air-tight container, with its contents clearly marked.

Products in glass jars and bottles such as jams, sauces and pickles can be stored in a cool, dry place until they are opened. After opening, it is wise to store the food in the fridge.

Tinned goods should be stored in a cool cupboard. Always put the new tins behind your existing stock, to minimise the risk of leaving a can forgotten in the corner.

Frozen food should be kept in a deep freeze or the freezer compartment of a fridge. There is a star rating found on these compartments which recommend how long food can be safely stored.

Food for storage in a fridge should be carefully sorted as shown in the diagram below.

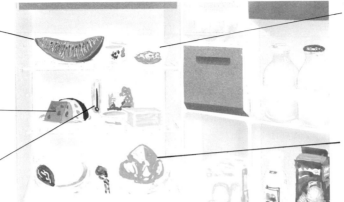

Food that is ready to eat is kept away from the raw foods below

All foods are individually wrapped or placed in shallow containers to avoid cross-contamination

Cheese and milk products are kept separate

A fridge thermometer placed in the middle of the fridge will indicate if the fridge is not at a safe temperature

Raw meats are kept well away from other foods and at the bottom of the refrigerator so that the meat juices cannot drip onto other foods

Freezers should be kept within a temperature range of –18°C to –23°C. A freezer thermometer could be installed so that you can make regular checks on the temperature.

All food should be labelled clearly with the purchase date, so that you know how long it has been in the freezer. You should also try to rotate stock, so that the oldest food is nearer the top and therefore used first.

If you do not have a freezer or freezer compartment, then frozen food should be kept in a fridge or other cool place and eaten within 24 hours. Frozen food, once thawed, should never be refrozen.

Never overstack a fridge or freezer. Air needs to be able to circulate freely to keep the temperature down. Fridges should ideally have a temperature of between 0°C and 3°C although a temperature of 7°C and below is acceptable. (Remember that some of the food poisoning bacteria, for example *Listeria*, are able to reproduce at a temperature of about 3°C.)

Kitchen hygiene

Kitchens should be clean, clutter-free and safe to work in. The ceilings and walls should not have peeling/flaking paint and should be regularly washed down. Surfaces should be clean and regularly washed with hot water and detergent to remove dirt and grease. The floor should be smooth and regularly washed. Food storage areas should be off the floor. Work surfaces should be smooth, without cracks or chips where dirt and microbes can get in. Sinks should be regularly cleaned.

Even kitchens which look clean can harbour dirt and microbes. For example, danger areas include under the work surface edges, the handles of cupboards, cracks in a chopping board, the space down the side of the cooker, the gap under the microwave, etc.

Many people are very fastidious about washing their hands, or keeping flies away, and then let their cats sleep on the work surfaces and eat out of the same bowls as the rest of the family. Keep a separate set of utensils and bowls for the pets, and keep them away from food preparation areas. Cats and dogs (and the creatures who live on them) can spread many microbes. Litter trays should not be kept in kitchens.

To avoid food-spoilage bacteria contaminating the kitchen it is best to have a very small bin, and empty it regularly. It should have a tight-fitting lid, which should always be closed. Always wash your hands after handling rubbish. The main dustbin should be situated well away from the kitchen.

Outdoor clothes and shoes should also be kept away from food areas to avoid contamination by soil bacteria.

There should be a plentiful supply of hot water and clean tea towels and dish cloths. Never use the same cloth for dishes and the floor.

Cleaning materials, floor cloths and brushes should be stored away from food.

Ideally, a good kitchen would have a separate basin for washing hands, but as this is often impractical in small kitchens, make sure that there is a good supply of soap and a separate towel for hand-washing. Never use a tea towel for drying your hands.

Even a clean looking kitchen may harbour bacteria and other potentially harmful organisms.

WHAT YOU CAN DO

1 Take a critical look at your kitchen. Write down a list of improvements which you should make.

2 Make up a checklist for people to use in their own kitchens.

Personal hygiene

In general, the cleaner you are, the less likely you are to contaminate food with microbes from your body or your clothes. Before preparing food you should ensure that you have thoroughly washed your hands, that your clothes and hair do not droop into the food (and are clean) and that you have removed hand jewellery and watches. Rings often trap dirt under the stones, and a watch sometimes stops you washing your hands, wrists and forearms properly for fear of getting it wet. If the food preparation is potentially messy, then wear a clean apron, made from a washable or easily wiped material.

Never comb or brush your hair in the kitchen, and avoid touching your nose and mouth as this can pass on potentially harmful microbes to other people. Wash your hands regularly especially after going to the toilet, handling raw foods, root vegetables, pets and rubbish. If in doubt, wash them again!

Do not smoke when in the kitchen, and never spit. It is a very unhygienic practice at any time and can pass on millions of microbes.

Any cuts or grazes should be covered with a waterproof dressing.

If you have been ill, especially if it was a stomach upset, avoid preparing food to reduce the risk of spreading the infection to others.

Preparing food safely

Careless food preparation can introduce harmful bacteria to food, which can then multiply and cause illness.

Recommended defrosting times.

	Defrosting times	
	In fridge	Room temperature
Chops and slices of boneless meat (per lb)	5 – 6 hrs	2 – 4 hrs
Joints of meat (less than 3 lb) (per lb)	3 – 4 hrs	1 – 2 hrs
Large joints of meat (more than 3 lb) (per lb)	6 – 7 hrs	2 – 3 hrs
Chicken portions (per portion)	12 – 24 hrs	6 – 8 hrs
Chicken and duck	1 – 2 days	1 day
Turkey and goose	2 – 3 days	2 days

Frozen food, especially meat and poultry, must be thawed properly, preferably in a fridge. If food is still frozen in the middle when it is cooked, the temperature which it reaches inside may not be high enough to kill the bacteria present even if the outside looks cooked and is piping hot. It is very important to follow any instructions given on food packaging about defrosting times to avoid this happening.

If food has to be defrosted out in the kitchen, it is important to ensure that it is covered to prevent any dust or flies landing on it.

Any water used in preparing food and drink should come from the mains supply, and not the hot tap, as water in the hot water system is often contained in a tank for some time, and is therefore not as clean as mains water.

Separate, non-wooden chopping boards, knives and other utensils should be used for raw and cooked foods. After preparing raw food, all the utensils should be thoroughly washed and dried before preparing anything else – even another raw food. Hands should be washed after handling raw food. Food that is dropped on the floor should be discarded.

When cooking joints of meat, it is wise to use a meat thermometer which will monitor the temperature at the centre of the joint. If this does not reach at least 70°C, then there is a danger that you have not destroyed the microbes in the meat. Poultry should also be cooked with care. Stuffing should be cooked separately in a dish and not inside the chicken, to ensure that the inside of the chicken will be hot enough, and that any bacteria present in the chicken does not contaminate the stuffing.

If you want to taste the food that you are preparing, use a clean spoon and wash it up immediately afterwards. If you need to taste the food again, use another spoon, again washing it as soon as you have finished.

If you are preparing food to be eaten at a later stage, cool it rapidly and then refrigerate it. It should be kept away from any raw food, it should be covered, and if it needs to be reheated, it should only be reheated once (see chapter 3, Food poisoning).

Testing the temperature of meat using a probe.

Is the temperature of the food in this cabinet correct?

PAUSE FOR THOUGHT

John, a first-year student at Newtown Polytechnic, was running late. He had invited two friends round to watch a video and had rashly said that he would cook them a meal. He had managed to rush out between his ten and eleven o'clock lectures, and do all the shopping. He was going to offer ice-cream as a pudding but had quickly realised that it would not survive the two-hour chemistry practical if it were stuffed in his rucksack under the bench. He decided to get some cheese instead.

He glanced at his watch. Six o'clock! Help! He quickly unpacked the rucksack. The cheese spread was a little soft and had oozed out a bit, but it had only landed on his squash shoes, so what the heck... He rushed over to the sink, took out yesterday's washing up and filled it from the hot tap so that he could warm up his hands whilst he peeled the potatoes. Rolling up his sleeves, he quickly peeled the potatoes, cut them up and put them on just in time. His hands were still cold, making him drop two of the potatoes on the floor. He quickly picked them up and gave them a wipe with the dish cloth.

After scraping the peelings off the board and into the bucket (the temporary bin) he started to shape the minced steak he had bought into nice, thick homemade burgers. Whilst he waited for the potatoes to boil and for the grill to heat up, he took the cheeses out of their wrappers and, giving the board a quick wipe with the dish cloth, he arranged the cheeses on the board and put them on the table, lifting the cat and the newspapers off the table. He then set the table, kicking the cat off again. Five minutes to go – just time to put the beans on. He took the half can from the fridge and added another can – a bargain from the supermarket as the can was dented. The grill was a bit high, and the burgers started to blacken but just as they did, his guests arrived and they sat down to their dinner.

On the whole the meal was a success, thought John. OK, so the beans were only just warm, and the burgers were a little red in the middle, but no one seemed to complain! They had a successful evening and drank a lot of beer, so that when they felt a little poorly in the morning, they put it down to too much beer.

1 *John and his friends enjoyed their meal, and blamed their stomach ache on a hangover. Write down a list of the unhygienic practices which you think John was carrying out.*

2 *Rewrite this story, taking into account the information in this chapter, showing how to avoid any contamination or unhygienic practice.*

3 *If John became very ill, what sort of food poisoning might he have? Write down his menu and, using the information in this book, work out which microbes might be present in the meal.*

Food poisoning

It is estimated that only a very small percentage of food poisoning cases ever get reported. This means that many sources are never traced because no one has reported being ill.

Early symptoms

The digestive system will react in different ways to different bacterial infections, but generally speaking, the main early symptoms are abdominal pain, vomiting and diarrhoea. The digestive system is a tube surrounded by involuntary muscle – muscle which we cannot control. When we have an infection, the muscles contract more than usual and move food towards the mouth and anus. Food and water are not absorbed into the body, so the faeces are watery.

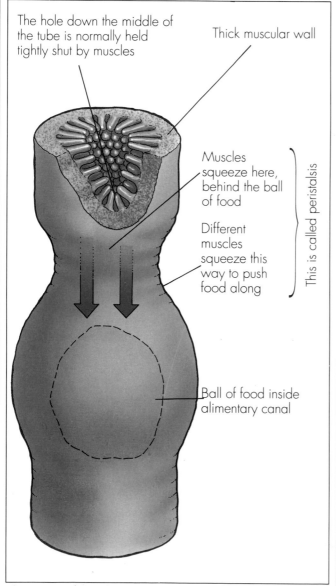

The hole down the middle of the tube is normally held tightly shut by muscles

Thick muscular wall

Muscles squeeze here, behind the ball of food

Different muscles squeeze this way to push food along

This is called peristalsis

Ball of food inside alimentary canal

The action of muscles surrounding the gut (alimentary canal).

Symptoms of food poisoning should never be ignored. It is especially important if the person is very young, very old or already ill as they are more likely to be seriously affected.

If food poisoning is suspected, then the doctor should be called. The doctor will try to alleviate the symptoms and will also question the patient about what he or she has eaten over the last 48 hours. The doctor will also try to discover if anyone else who has eaten the same foods is similarly affected. Any food remaining from the suspect meal should be carefully kept, and the bin should not be emptied.

One of the principal causes for concern with food poisoning is dehydration, especially in babies and toddlers. If diarrhoea persists for longer than a couple of hours whatever the cause, the doctor must be called. All patients should be encouraged to sip diluted fruit juice or warmed water from a mains cold tap supply, to which a teaspoon of sugar and a pinch of salt has been added. A cola drink which has been allowed to lose its fizz can also help as it will rehydrate the patient and also replace some of the salt lost and provide some sugar for energy.

The symptoms of food poisoning from chemical poisons or poisonous metals can start as soon as ten minutes after eating the contaminated food, whilst the symptoms from listeria, for example, may not appear for a number of weeks. If it is fairly certain which food was contaminated because, for example, all the people who consumed the food are affected, the length of time for the symptoms to appear may help with diagnosis of the disease. Often it is impossible to tell which food was contaminated until the causative organism has been identified. When it has, the food eaten at the approximate time of infection can be investigated.

The doctor will take samples of faeces and perhaps a sample of blood for analysis by the public health laboratories from the affected person(s). The environmental health department of the local council will be informed by the doctor, and the detective work can begin.

To find the cause of the food poisoning, the faecal samples are taken and grown on plated agar jelly in carefully controlled conditions. These conditions are favourable to most bacteria, and, by allowing the bacteria to reproduce, colonies large enough to be identified will be produced, even from a single bacterium. This process can take up to 24 hours.

In the meantime, if a number of people are affected, an Environmental Health Officer will visit the house or food outlet where the suspected food was eaten, and take away samples of food, food waste or even discarded

TYPE OF FOOD POISONING	INCUBATION PERIOD	SYMPTOMS
Salmonella	12 hours–2 days	Abdominal pains, diarrhoea, dehydration, exhaustion.
Campylobacter	3–7 days	Abdominal pains, bloody diarrhoea, exhaustion.
Listeria	5 days–5 weeks	Flu-like symptoms, few gut symptoms, stillbirth, septicaemia meningitis.
Bacillus cereus	6–18 hours	Diarrhoea, abdominal pains.
Botulism	12–18 hours	Nausea, vomiting, followed by progressive paralysis of nerves affecting movement.
Clostridium perfringens	8–22 hours	Diarrhoea, abdominal pain.
Staphylococcal	30 minutes–6 hours	Vomiting, often with the appearance of blood.

The symptoms of food poisoning.

food containers so that the contents can be analysed. After finding out exactly what the ill people have eaten over the last 48 hours, the Officer can then work out the most likely sources of contamination by working out which food was eaten by everyone. If the cause of contamination was food eaten at a restaurant, café or other food outlet, then the Environmental Health Officer will visit the premises. This will be as soon as possible after the department has been notified. The Officer takes food samples, and checks for any unhygienic practices. Samples and swabs may be taken from the staff working there as well, in case one of them is a carrier and is passing on the bacteria because of poor personal hygiene.

If you suspect a restaurant of unhygienic practices or of causing your food poisoning, it is advisable not to contact them yourself. This will give unscrupulous owners and managers sufficient warning to dispose of any evidence before the Environmental Health Officers visit and also it may not lead to any permanent change in the way food is stored and prepared. If the Officer visits without any warning, however, he or she will get a more accurate picture of the food-handling procedures which may have contributed to the outbreak of food poisoning.

If a food outlet persists in breaking the hygiene regulations, then the Environmental Health Officer can serve an Order closing the establishment down. Very often, the restaurants will voluntarily close, and spend time updating their kitchen facilities so that they do not contravene any health regulations. In 1986, there were 907 prosecutions under the 1970 Food Hygiene (General) Regulations, which indicates that there is still a real problem.

Microbiology lab, where tests would be carried out to check the safety of food supplies.

Environmental health departments run certificated courses for food handlers to increase their awareness of food hygiene and safe practices in commercial kitchens. It is far better to prevent food poisoning than it is to deal with the results.

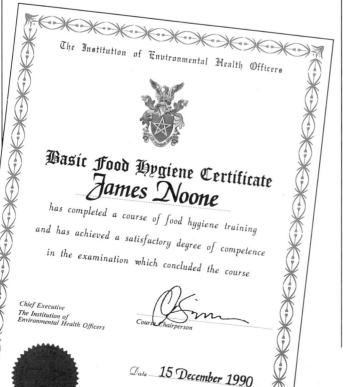

The Institution of Environmental Health Officers

Basic Food Hygiene Certificate
James Noone

has completed a course of food hygiene training
and has achieved a satisfactory degree of competence
in the examination which concluded the course

Chief Executive
The Institution of
Environmental Health Officers

Course Chairperson

Date 15 December 1990

WHAT YOU CAN DO

Read the following cases and, using the information in this book, try to work out:
a) the food causing the food poisoning;
b) the disease (if not mentioned);
c) the bad practices which have led to the food poisoning.

CASE NUMBER 1

It was a hot summer and in the streets of Newtown, the street vendors were doing a roaring trade selling ice-cream and soft drinks. The Environmental Health Officer was notified of 25 cases of acute gastric illness which was later identified as typhoid. It appeared that all the people affected had been eating ice-cream cones bought from one of the largest ice-cream makers in the area. The officer visited the factory where the ice-cream was made and could find no trace of *Salmonella typhi* in the ice-cream or the sugar cones. All the delivery vehicles were in good order. Eventually it was discovered that all the cases had come from one particular stall. The stall and all its containers were clear of *Salmonella typhi*, but the bacteria were present on the ice-cream scoop and some cones.

CASE NUMBER 2

Five people who had eaten at a local restaurant complained to the local council after being taken ill. Most had experienced the same symptoms – abdominal pains, chronic diarrhoea – about 12 hours after eating. The foods that they ate were:

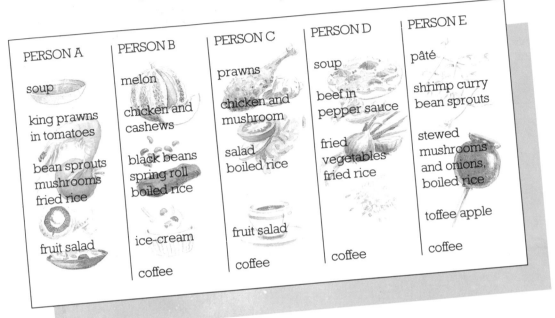

PERSON A
soup

king prawns in tomatoes

bean sprouts mushrooms fried rice

fruit salad

PERSON B
melon

chicken and cashews

black beans spring roll boiled rice

ice-cream

coffee

PERSON C
prawns

chicken and mushroom

salad boiled rice

fruit salad

coffee

PERSON D
soup

beef in pepper sauce

fried vegetables fried rice

coffee

PERSON E
pâté

shrimp curry bean sprouts

stewed mushrooms and onions, boiled rice

toffee apple

coffee

When the Environmental Health Officer visited the kitchens he found them in generally good order. All the food was in separate, clean containers. The cooking pots were regularly washed, the staff were clean and dressed in clean protective clothing. The food was being cooked as the orders came in. To speed up the service, the rice was made in a large batch and left in a large bowl covered by a clean cloth ready to fry or heat through.

CASE NUMBER 3

After a traditional roast dinner of beef, gravy, roast potatoes, sprouts, carrots and Yorkshire pudding, followed by apple pie and custard, the Robinson family all fell ill. They all had acute abdominal pains and diarrhoea which appeared about 14 hours after eating the meal. After questioning the family, it appears that the beef and gravy were cooked by the grandmother two days before, and left to cool for six hours then refrigerated. She packed the meat in a polythene box and carefully put it on the back shelf of the car to drive the 200-mile journey to her daughter's house. The gravy was transported in a vacuum flask. The meat was reheated just before serving.

GLOSSARY

Additive – a substance added to food which is not normally eaten as a food by itself, such as preservatives, emulsifiers, stabilisers, colouring, flavouring.

Aerobic (respiration) – using oxygen (to release energy from food).

Anaerobic (respiration) – using little or no oxygen (to release energy from food).

Antibody – proteins made by the body which react with and help to destroy invading microbes.

Antiseptic – a substance which kills microbes and can be used safely on human tissue.

Antigens – substances found on microbes which stimulate antibody production.

Bacteria – one-celled, simple, living micro-organisms.

Balanced diet – a diet containing the right amount of all the nutrients that the human body requires.

Best before – a date found on packaged food, to inform the consumer how long the 'shelf-life' of the product is.

Binary fission – a type of reproduction, where the organism divides into two, producing two identical daughter cells.

Biotechnology – the use of microbes and plant and animal cells by humans to produce useful substances.

Causative organism – the organism responsible for causing a disease or disorder.

Chemical fertiliser – chemicals used in farming to increase the yield and/or quality of a crop by providing the mineral ions which the plant needs.

Contamination – the infection or pollution of a substance. This can be accidental or deliberate.

Cook-chill – the method of food preparation where food is prepared, cooked, rapidly chilled and kept in a chilled cabinet for reheating at a later stage.

Decay – to break down (rot) plant or animal material into its component chemicals. This is an important part of the recycling process of nutrients.

Decomposer – an organism which carries out the process of decomposition (breaking down) leading to decay.

Dehydrate – to remove water, to make dry.

Developed country – a term used to describe the richer nations of the world. They are normally highly industrialised.

Digestion – the process which breaks down food into its simple units so that it can be absorbed into the body through the gut. Digestion is carried out by enzymes.

Disease – a state which affects the normal working of the body (dis-ease) leading to an unhealthy condition.

Disinfectant – a substance which kills microbes, used for the scrupulous cleaning of objects. Disinfectants should not be used on human tissue.

Endospore – type of spore produced by bacteria when conditions are unfavourable. They can withstand drying, some disinfectants and greater heat than other living things.

Environmental Health Officer – experienced, highly trained individuals whose expertise includes pollution control, food safety, occupational health and safety and housing standards. In the area of food safety they are employed to ensure the maintenance of high standards of hygiene and the production of safe, wholesome food. Although they are responsible for enforcing food legislation, they are always available to give guidance and advice.

Enzyme – a type of protein that speeds up a biological process and is unchanged by it.

Food- and water-borne disease – diseases carried in food or water.

Food poisoning – illness caused by eating contaminated food containing large numbers of food-poisoning microbes.

Food spoilage – the breaking down of food by microbes, rendering the food inedible.

Fungi – a group of microbes, commonly called moulds, which feed on plant and animal matter by producing digestive juice and absorbing the digested food through hyphae (branching strands).

Hygiene – the practice of maintaining health through cleanliness.

Immune system – the human system which fights infection from invading micro-organisms by producing antibodies and engulfing foreign bodies.

Immunity – the ability of an organism to resist infection from an invading organism so that the body does not develop the disease.

Infected – contaminated with micro-organisms.

Infestation – when a person or place is invaded/overrun with pests, vermin or disease.

Irradiation – exposing items to the action of γ (gamma) radiation from a radioactive source.

Irrigation – supplying dry land with water by digging channels and sinking wells.

Latrines – toilets/places where people urinate and defaecate. These can be as simple as pits in the ground.

Legislation – laws.

Micro-organism – a microscopic organism which is capable of a separate existence.

Offal – parts often regarded as waste from animal carcases, eg entrails, lungs, liver, kidneys, brain, spinal cord.

Osmosis – the movement of water from a weak to a strong solution across differentially permeable membrane.

Pathogenic – disease-causing.

Pest – organisms which are harmful to us either directly or by affecting the food we eat.

Pesticide residue – traces of chemical used for destroying pests on crops which is left on food, eg fresh fruit and vegetables.

Preservation – making food last longer by treating it in some way.

Radiation – particles emitted from radioactive materials which can be dangerous to plants and animals if not properly controlled.

Spore – single-celled bodies produced by bacteria and fungi. These are small and light and can disperse the organism. Some spores have a thick, protective wall and are difficult to destroy.

Stock rotation – the system whereby the oldest food is sold first, with the new stock placed at the back of shelves and stores.

Symptom – a noticeable change which may be a sign of an infection, injury or disease.

Toxin – poison, sometimes produced by a pathogenic organism in the body.

Transmission – the passing-on of a disease-causing organism from one person (or organism) to another.

Use by – date found on the label/packaging of food if the food is highly perishable (day, date).

Vector – an organism which transmits the causative micro-organism of a disease from one individual to another. Flies and mosquitoes are examples of vectors.

Vermin – creatures regarded as harmful to game, crops and food stores, eg rats, mice, foxes, insects (cockroaches, flies, beetles, fleas, lice) and some worms.

INDEX